Nature
COLOR BY NUMBERS

Nature
COLOR BY NUMBERS

Compiled by
Felicity James

ARCTURUS

Illustrations by Else Lennox,
Arpad Olbey, Nathalie Ortega,
Martin Sanders, Sara Storino
and David Woodroffe.

ARCTURUS

This edition published in 2019 by Arcturus Publishing Limited
26/27 Bickels Yard, 151–153 Bermondsey Street,
London SE1 3HA.

ISBN: 978-1-78950-052-3
CH006906NT
Supplier 29, Date 0119, Print run 8071

Printed in China

Created for children 10+

Introduction

This collection of color-by-numbers images celebrates the natural world in all its beauty and variety. The many forms of life on our planet make wonderful subjects for the artist, from the tiniest insects to the greatest panoramic views.

The artworks in this book will deepen your appreciation of the natural world, as well as improving your coloring skills and dexterity. Many images focus on wildlife from around the globe, including butterflies, birds, fish, and reptiles – all set in their natural environments. Among the larger animals are a stag, horses, a polar bear, a lion, and a rhinoceros.

The collection also includes many beautiful landscapes, from breath-taking mountains to desert and coastal scenes. Some views will be instantly recognizable, like the iconic Grand Canyon in Arizona, USA, and the timeworn, magical monolith called Uluru (or Ayers Rock), to be found in Australia's outback.

Looking beyond these natural wonders, the nature that many of us encounter day to day is in the form of flowers and trees. You will find detailed artworks of flowers to color, including sunflowers, poppies, and snowdrops, as well as woodland scenes and a mesmerizing ancient tree.

Each image is fully numbered so that you can build up an impressive artwork. Using the color key on the cover, match your set of colored pencils to the colors in the key. If there is no number that means the space should be left white or colored with a white pencil.

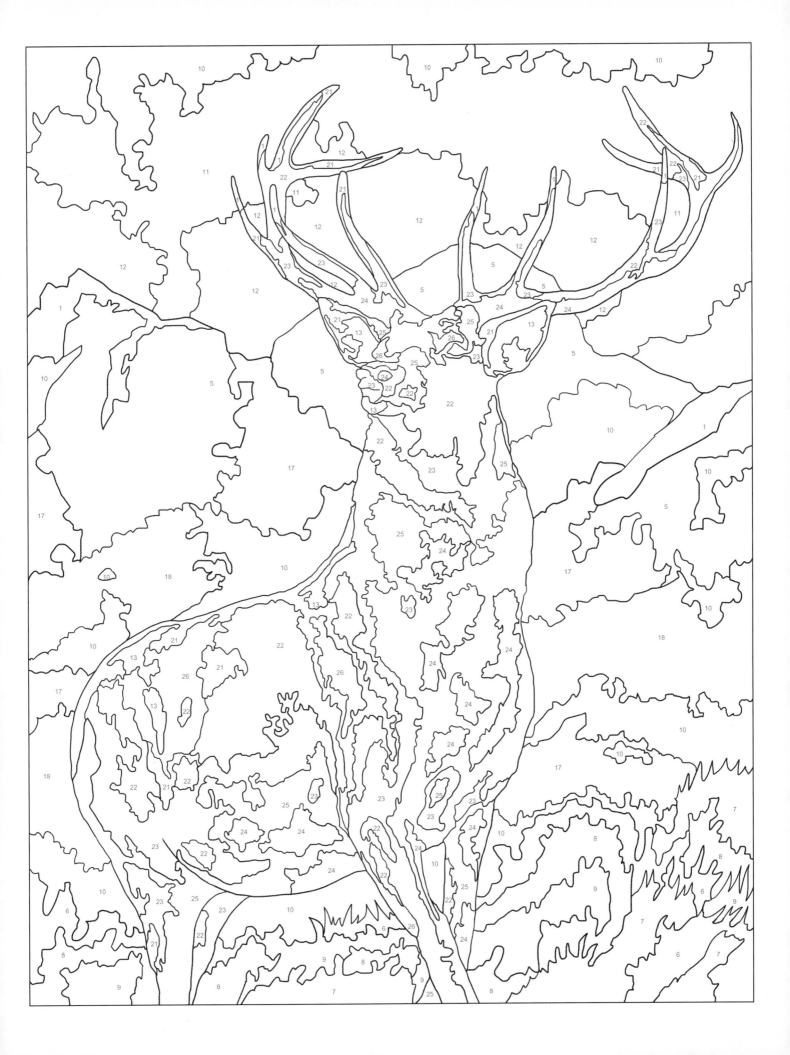

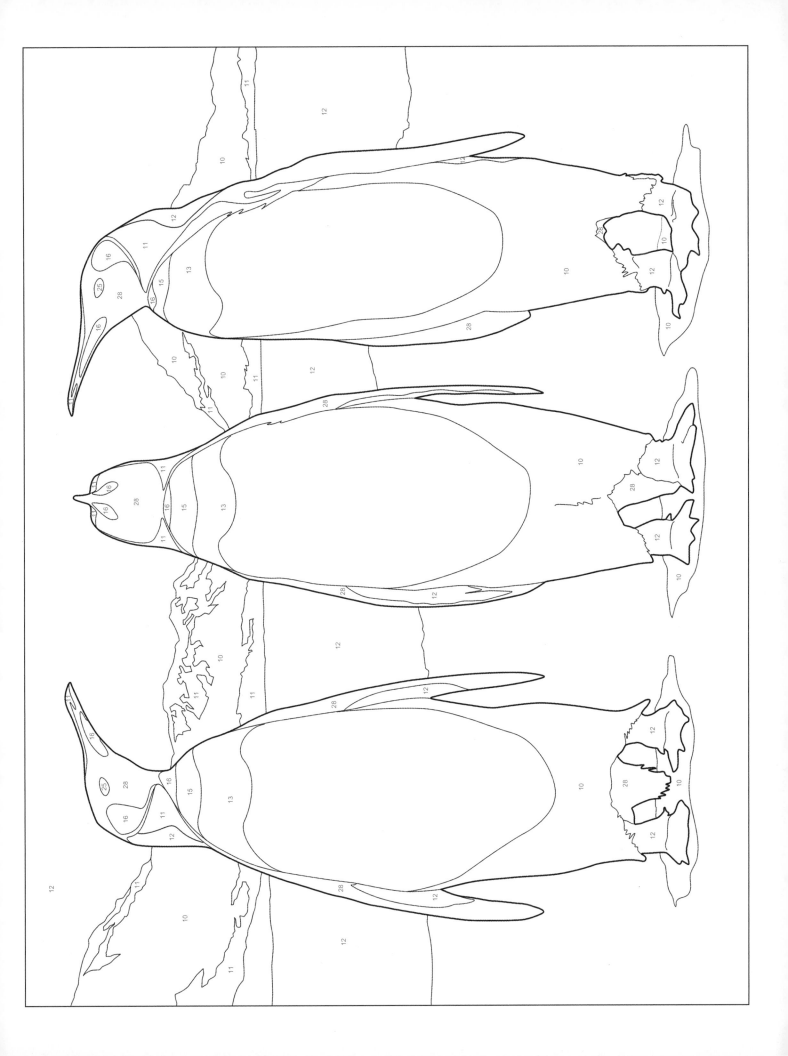

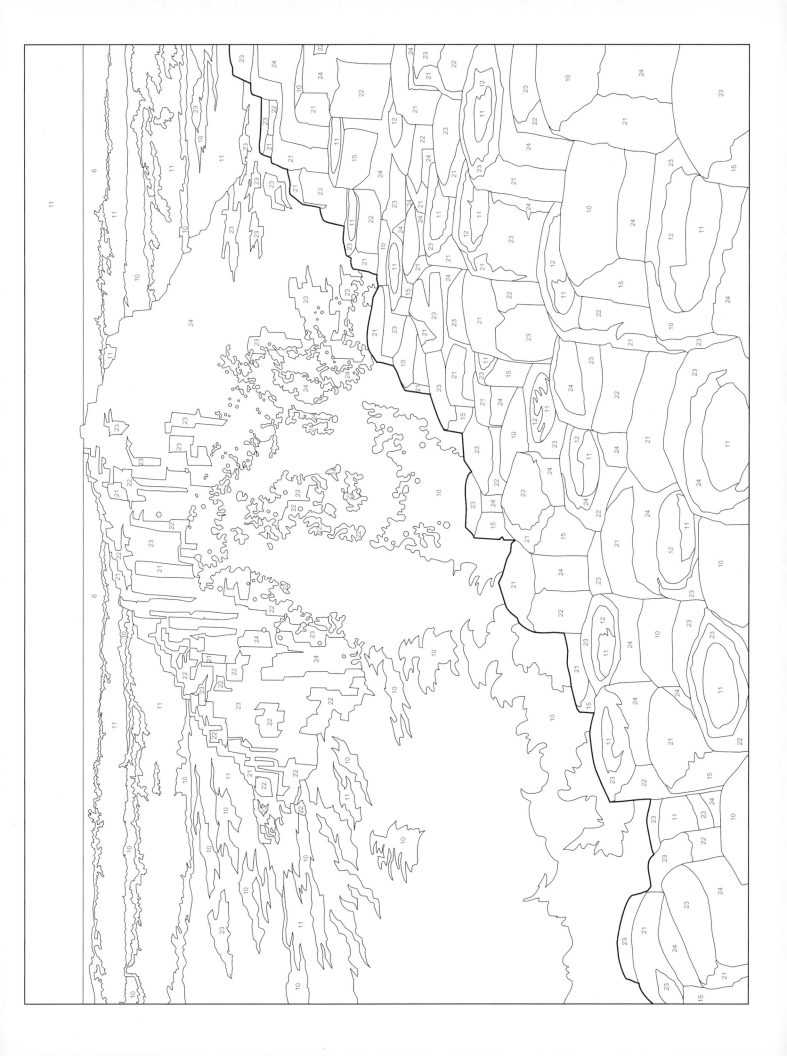

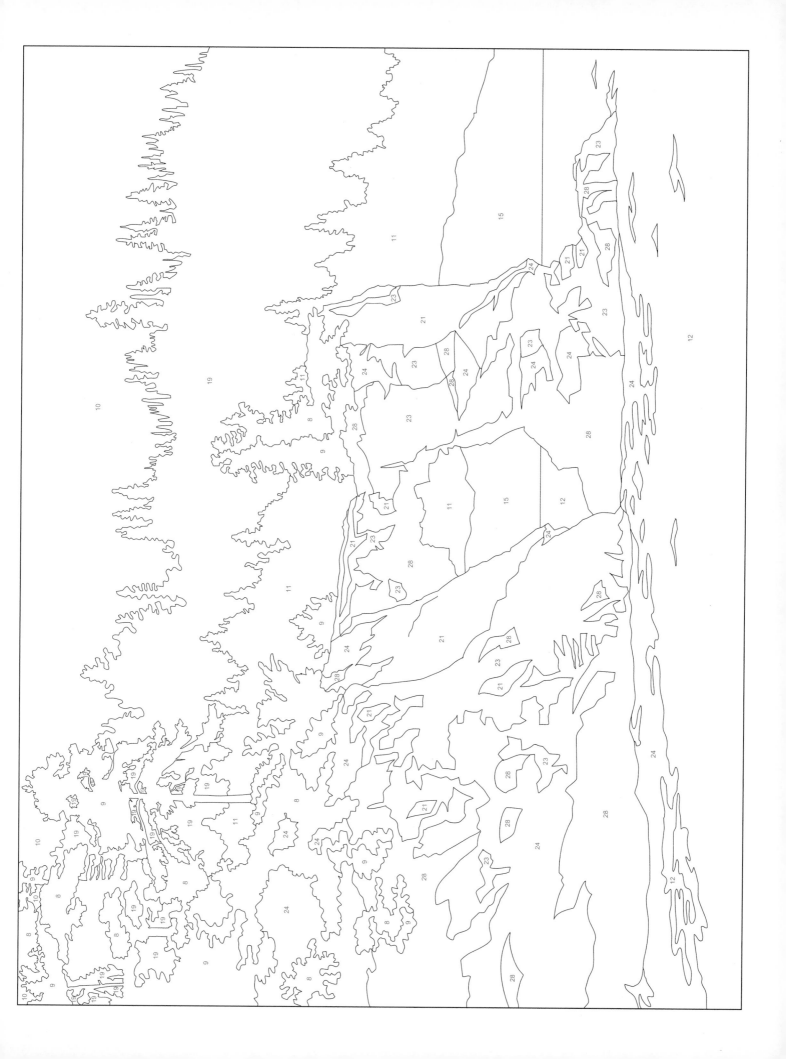

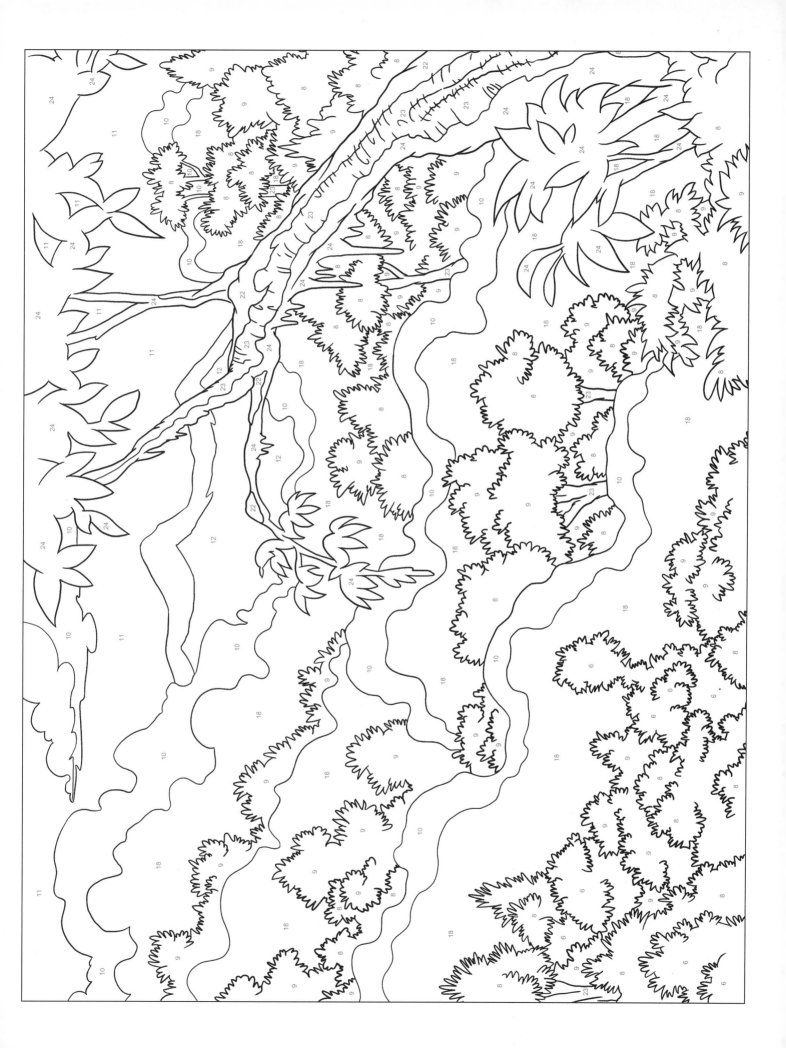

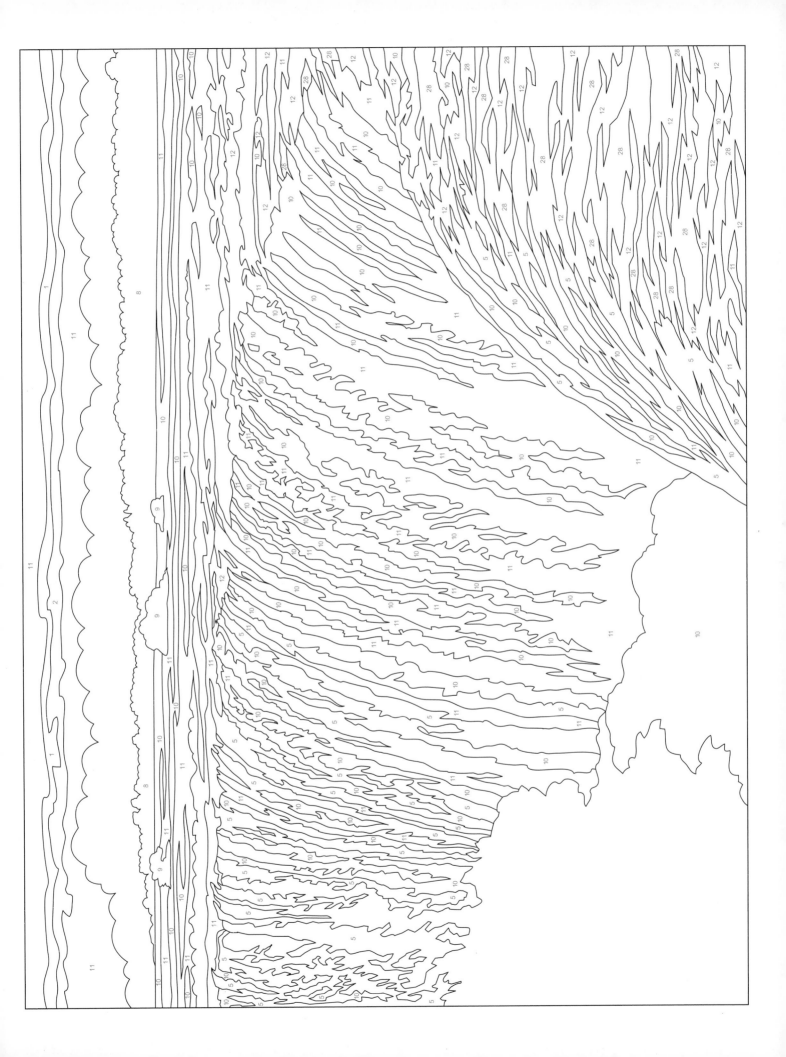

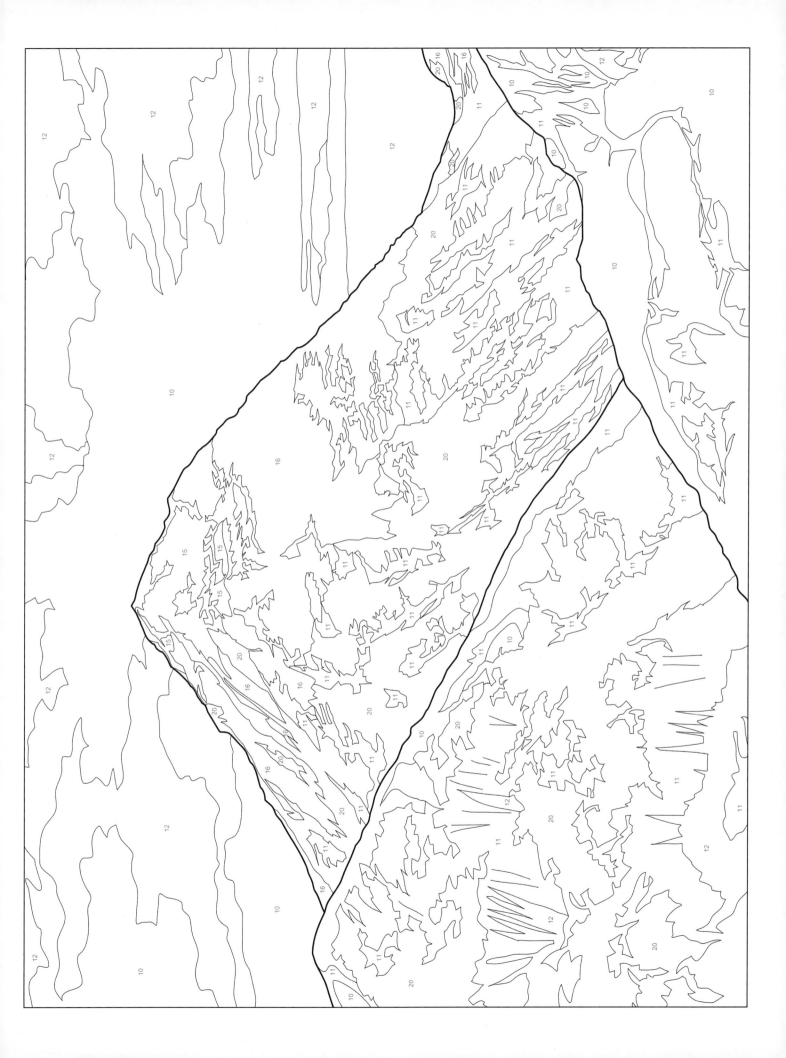